CW00687384

VOICE for LIFE

SINGER'S WORKBOOK 5: YELLOW LEVEL

CONTENTS

This book belongs to

_____

of

_____ choir.

VOICE for LIFE

Project editor: Tim Ruffer

Written and edited by Catherine Duffy, Anthony Marks and Leah Perona-Wright

This edition fully revised and updated by Anthony Marks

Voice for Life was developed by Leah Perona-Wright in consultation with experienced practitioners from across the UK and beyond. These include: Gordon Appleton, Colin Baldy, Roger Brice, Chris Broughton, Lesley Cooper, June Cox, Colin Davey, Paul Ellis, Peter Futcher, Susan Gardner, Ameral Gunson, John Harper, Esther Jones, Sally Leeming, Hilary Llystyn Jones, Sue Moore, David Ogden, Keith Roberts, Sheila Robertson, Ben Saunders, John Wardle, Alistair Warwick, Geoff Weaver and Jenevora Williams. We are grateful for their contributions.

Design and layout: Anthony Marks and Catherine Duffy
Music origination: Leah Perona-Wright and Anthony Marks
Illustrations: Hilary Perona-Wright
Editorial assistance: Julian Elloway and Sally Ruffer

This collection, its typography, artwork and layout are
copyright © 2004, 2012 The Royal School of Church Music

All rights reserved. No part of this publication may be reproduced, stored in a retrieval system, or transmitted, in any form or by any means, without the prior permission in writing of the copyright holder, or as expressly permitted by law.

Printed in Great Britain by Caligraving Ltd, Thetford

ISBN 978-0-85402-215-1

THE ROYAL SCHOOL OF CHURCH MUSIC
19 The Close, Salisbury, Wiltshire, SP1 2EB
Tel: +44 (0)1722 424848   Fax: +44 (0)1722 424849
E-mail: education@rscm.com Website: www.rscm.com
Registered charity no. 312828

Distributed exclusively in North America by GIA Publications, Inc.
7404 S. Mason Ave., Chicago, IL 60638
Toll free: 800 442 1358 Website: www.giamusic.com

Welcome to *Voice for Life*. It is designed to help you discover what your voice can do, and then strengthen it. It will encourage you to learn about music and look at what it means to be a singer and a member of a choir.

This workbook will help you to practise singing and think about music at home, but you will also work closely with your choir trainer. Together you will discuss which topic to work on next – don't try to complete the whole book on your own in one week! Your choir trainer may want to explain a new topic before you go further through the book, or to talk to you at rehearsals about things you should do on your own. He or she may also want to check that you have understood something before you move on to the next stage.

To make the most of your voice, you need to practise regularly. This workbook contains breathing and singing exercises to use at home. If you practise on your own as well as with your choir, you will quickly improve the strength of your voice. As a singer, your whole body is your musical instrument – you take it to bed, on the bus, in the car, shopping, to parties and even on holiday – so it makes sense to take care of all aspects of it. To help you look after your voice, there are tips on voice care throughout the book.

This workbook contains activities and exercises to complete in your own time. You will also be expected to talk to other members of your choir to find the answers to some of the questions. Don't worry about doing this – other choir members expect to be asked for information or advice. You will find it useful to have a separate notebook or file to use when completing some of the activities.

Being in a choir is different from being a solo singer. You are a member of a team. You will learn about being a good team member, making the best contribution you can to your choir, and helping less experienced singers.

To complete the Yellow level of *Voice for Life*, you must achieve the targets listed on pages 46–50. Some targets are about your progress during choir rehearsals, services and concerts; others are about things you will do in your own time. As you work through them, you will improve as a singer and choir member. After you complete each one, your choir trainer will sign its box. You can find out what happens when you complete all the targets inside the back cover. There is a reference section on pages 51–54 and an index on pages 55–56.

Enjoy *Voice for Life!*

Lindsay Gray

Lindsay Gray
Director, RSCM

Icons   The icons in this book tell you to:

 Read this before going further

 Try a vocal or physical exercise

 Sing something

 Think about something

 Write an answer in the box

 Tick when you have finished an activity

Posture

 Much of our communication is due to our body language, rather than the words that we say. Your body language and facial expressions can tell others that you are relaxed, frightened, angry, defensive, or confident, even if your words do not. Likewise, even before you start to sing, your posture makes an impression on your listeners. Posture is an important part of showing confidence and professionalism.

Confident?

Miserable?

Consider a performer's posture from the perspective of the audience. Singers who stand well create an impact before they even begin to sing. They look focused and professional. The audience can relax and enjoy the music with confidence.

Angry?

Your posture also affects your singing voice. Good posture allows the muscles to function to their optimum level, whereas bad posture impairs the working of the muscles and, therefore, the voice. Any tension in the body can be heard when you sing, so it is important to develop and maintain good posture.

Posture has a significant effect on our general health and well-being. For example, bad posture over a long period of time can produce serious neck and back pain. We need to be aware of our posture at all times – not just when singing.

 If you stand properly, your head, body and legs will be in alignment. This frees your body of tension and makes singing easier. The diagram on the right shows how the mouth, larynx and spinal column are linked in vertical alignment. See how this relates to your own posture. Mark on the diagram any places where you feel you need to improve the way you stand. Here are a few tips to help you.

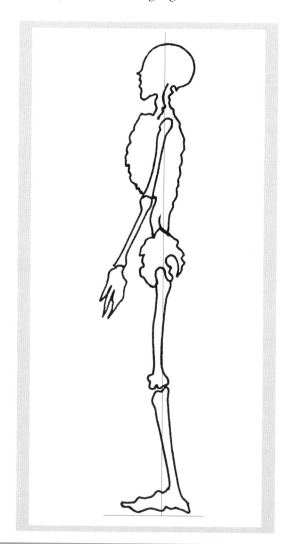

 • Keep your spine straight (aligned as shown in the diagram). This allows your diaphragm to work properly and helps your back muscles to support the sound.

• Do not let your shoulders sag, or your head move too far forward, as this impairs the working of the neck muscles.

• Your head weighs about 15lb (over 6kg). If it is in the wrong position, your muscles have to work harder to keep your body balanced. (If you have to sing while kneeling, be careful to balance your head properly without pushing your chin forward.)

Your body is your musical instrument. Take care of it every day. Think about your posture often – when standing in a queue, while chatting or cooking. Good posture helps the flow of blood and oxygen throughout the body, releasing tensions and making you feel fitter and more energetic. You could ask your choir trainer for more advice about your own posture and how to improve it. Here are some hints.

Stretching the spine

 Singing often involves long periods of standing. If the area around your lower spine aches after standing for a while, this could be because it is too curved. Try stretching the base of your spine with this exercise.

Place your hands on your hips, with your thumbs on the hip bone at the front and the fingers behind.

 Bend your knees slightly. Turn your pelvis by moving your thumbs upwards and backwards slightly while your fingers move downwards and forwards.

 The following exercises will help you to compare good and bad posture, and the corresponding effects on your body and your vocal production.

Relaxed or locked knees?

 Stand up straight with your body balanced. Relax your shoulders, put your hands down by your side, and relax your knees. Keep your head and spine straight, and your breathing steady and natural. Breathe in and out a few times.

Now lock your knees (push them back as far as you can) and breathe in and out a few times, as naturally as possible. You will begin to feel that your breathing has become restricted and that there is tension in the lower abdomen and up towards the throat. Unlock your knees once more, and breathe again to feel the difference. Try this when leaning your body weight to one side and locking one knee. You will find that this affects your breathing too.

The effect of balance and tension

 In your bare feet, walk around the room singing a simple song. Now walk on tiptoe and do the same exercise. Can you feel your leg muscles stretching? Can you feel how your body has to adjust the balance and position of your head? You may also find that you cannot reach high notes as easily.

Try this exercise with another singer. While one of you sings, the other should listen to hear the difference in the timbre of the voice. Then swap over.

Bear in mind that shoes with a heel higher than 4cm force the body to re-adjust and balance itself. This can affect the quality of the voice.

Relaxing the shoulders

 Keep your shoulders relaxed at all times as tension will affect your voice. Raise your shoulders up as far as you can. Drop them a little, and then drop them again to release tension in the shoulders. Compare the feeling of tense and relaxed shoulders.

What happens when you breathe

The diaphragm is the main muscle used in inhalation. Although its effects can be detected, it is not possible to feel or control it directly.

As you inhale, the diaphragm descends (contracts), pulling the bottom of the lungs down, and creating a vacuum which causes the air to rush in. When the lungs fill with air, the lower ribs expand outward, and the waistline also expands.

As you exhale, the process is reversed: the diaphragm relaxes, being pushed upward by the abdominal muscles. This causes the lower ribs to contract inward, resulting in a contraction of the body around the waistline.

 On the diagrams below, mark with arrows the movement of the lungs, diaphragm and waistline during inhalation and exhalation. Refer to the explanation above.

Inhalation

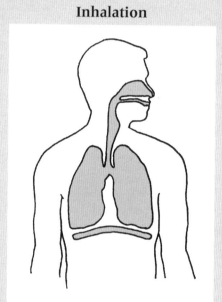

Exhalation

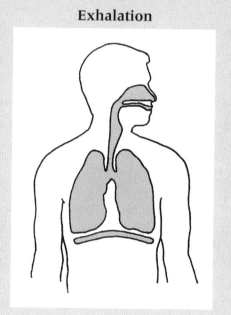

 Breathing exercises

Breathing correctly is fundamental to good singing: it affects dynamics, phrasing, tuning and tone. Breathing exercises can help all singers. To begin your practice, try the following exercise. This should help to ensure that your throat is relaxed.

 Placing the voice in neutral

Stand up straight, with your feet slightly apart, and make a panting sound, like a dog. The diaphragm is moving up and down in the way described above. Make sure that your throat or mouth are not tense. Try not to force the breath out, as this will dry out the vocal folds and could close the throat. Instead, aim for a gentle in-and-out movement of breath and use equal effort in inhalation and exhalation.

Simple breathing is something that you do all the time without thinking about it. This exercise helps you to use this natural reflex. It is a good way to remove tension and put the voice back into neutral (its normal, relaxed state). This will prevent you getting vocally tired.

The excited diaphragm
Having relaxed your throat, use the following exercise to prepare your diaphragm for singing. Place the voice into 'neutral' again (see previous page). This time, do it in such a way that you bring a sense of excitement to the movement. Take in a breath, maintaining this feeling of excitement. With the 'excited diaphragm' working all the time, it should be possible to sing long, supported notes and phrases more easily.

 Using the excited diaphragm
Choose a comfortable note to begin the exercise below. Repeat both sets of vowels several times. Each time you repeat, move up or down a semitone. You may find the exercise tiring at first, but this demonstrates that the correct muscles are working. It should not feel painful or uncomfortable, however.

oo ee oo ee oo ee oo ee oo ee oo ee oo ee oo ee oo
ah ee ah ee ah ee ah ee ah ee ah ee ah ee ah ee ah

 Having mastered these diaphragm exercises, you should always prepare your voice for singing by using this level of excitement. This makes the diaphragm work hard and helps you to sing with intensity. The following exercise builds on this.

 Breathing warm-up
This is a very good exercise to use for warming-up. It is based on the 'Placing the voice in neutral' exercise, but this time you should vocalise on the outward movement and inhale at every rest. Practise singing this exercise using both 'ah' and 'oo' sounds. With each repetition, move the starting note up or down a semitone. Gradually increase the speed of the exercise.

ah   ah   ah   ah   ah   ah   ah   ah
oo   oo   oo   oo   oo   oo   oo   oo

 Singing with intensity
Sing one of the following phrases from Handel's *Messiah*:

- Baritones and basses: 'For behold, darkness shall cover the earth

- Tenors: 'He was cut off out of the land of the living'

- Counter-tenors: 'Then shall be brought to pass'

- Altos: 'Behold a virgin shall conceive' or 'Then shall the eyes of the blind' (alto version)

- Sopranos: 'And the angel said unto them' or 'Then shall the eyes of the blind' (soprano version)

 Imagine you are excited, but forbidden to make a sound – like trying not to laugh in church. Keep this in mind while singing the phrase. It might seem as if you are trying to suppress the sound, but as long as this only happens in the diaphragm and not in the throat, you will be working hard to support the sound without singing *forte*.

In this way, you should be able to sing with a high level of intensity. As you will have discovered, you always have to work harder when singing quietly.

Breathing

Using and developing the back muscles
The back is covered in muscle and is much stronger than the front of the body. The muscles in the back can be used to support your voice. This enables you to draw on a far larger range of muscles than just the diaphragm; it also helps avoid over-use of the diaphragm.

The main back muscles that support the sound are the *latissimus dorsi* and the *quadratus lumborum* (see diagram). The exercises below use these muscles. But you can use other muscles too (notably the *trapezius* which runs from just below the middle of the spine to the neck).

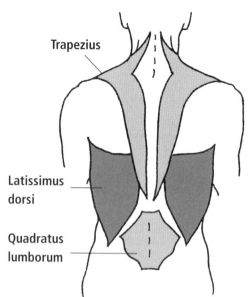

The sensation of using the back muscles

Exhale sharply. One of the functions of the *quadratus* is to cause this movement. If you used enough effort, the *latissimus* will have helped out too. Did you feel your back muscles tightening? Now bend forwards and rest your hands on your lower back. Try to feel your flanks (the fleshy area that runs down from your back across your hips). Now exhale sharply again. Did you feel the muscles working that time?

Strengthening the back muscles

Choose a comfortable starting note. Repeat the exercise several times, moving up a tone each time. Before singing each phrase, exhale forcefully. It may seem strange to sing after exhaling, but this forces the back muscles to support the sound. Take care not to close your throat: the air needs to pass through without hindrance.

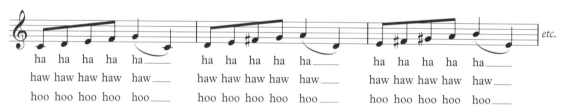

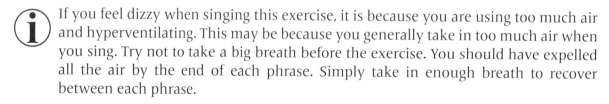

Aim to reach the point where your back muscles feel just slightly tired. With practice, it should get easier and the muscles will strengthen. You will then find that these muscles are working as you sing and you will not keep running out of breath.

If you feel dizzy when singing this exercise, it is because you are using too much air and hyperventilating. This may be because you generally take in too much air when you sing. Try not to take a big breath before the exercise. You should have expelled all the air by the end of each phrase. Simply take in enough breath to recover between each phrase.

VOICE CARE TIP
When rehearsing in a cold church or hall, it is natural to raise your shoulders to try to keep warm. But this actually makes you colder because it limits the blood supply to the heart. It also tightens the throat muscles, which can lead to tension in the jaw. Relaxing the shoulders allows the blood to circulate more easily, which will keep you warmer than if you raise them.

Vocal sound is produced by vibrations in the larynx (voice box). The larynx is at the top of the trachea (windpipe), and is made of cartilage. The parts of the larynx that vibrate are the vocal folds, which lie horizontally across the thyroid cartilage.

The diagrams below show the parts of the neck and throat that are involved in voice production. As you do the exercises below, it may help you to refer back to them to remind yourself of the different parts and what they are called.

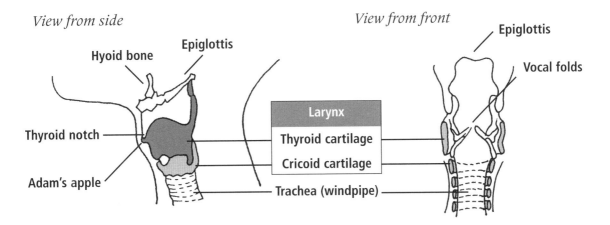

View from side *View from front*

Hyoid bone Epiglottis Epiglottis

Vocal folds

Thyroid notch

Larynx

Thyroid cartilage

Cricoid cartilage

Adam's apple

Trachea (windpipe)

The vocal folds
 The vocal folds are sometimes called vocal cords, but as they are made up of several parts, 'folds' is more accurate. They are about as long as the width of a finger nail. For them to work properly, the larynx must be able to move up and down and tilt freely. If it becomes crushed or fixed while you sing, the sound will be badly affected.

 The exercises below will help you achieve this, but it is extremely important that you work slowly and gently. Before you start, discuss them with your choir trainer, a singing teacher, or an experienced singer. If you feel the slightest discomfort, stop.

Finding the larynx
 Study the diagrams above and find the thyroid notch with your index finger. This is the V-shaped indentation at the top of the Adam's apple (a projection of the thyroid cartilage). It is usually more prominent in men.

 Gently place your thumb and middle finger either side of this notch and move them backwards along the top of the thyroid cartilage. You'll notice that they rise and then fall as they follow the shape of the cartilage. About a centimetre back you will feel two small 'horns' sticking up. On top of this sits the hyoid bone, sometimes called the tongue bone because the base of the tongue is attached to it.

Remember this construction because it is important that the hyoid bone is always free when singing. If the tongue pushes down on it, the sound produced will be rather unnatural and swallowed. Similarly, if you have 'fixed' the hyoid bone with the muscles in front of it, you will produce a tight sound.

 Try holding your hyoid bone between your thumb and index finger and see whether you can move it from side to side. Be very gentle! It should move easily and freely about one centimetre in each direction. Having checked that the hyoid bone is flexible, try moving the whole larynx from side to side (again, be gentle).

Tone and range

 If the larynx is too high when you sing, you will produce a strangled sound. If it is too low, you will produce a swallowed sound. It is important to sing with the larynx in the correct position. To do this, you need to neutralize the muscles under the jaw and around your hyoid bone. This 'releases' the larynx. Regular use of the exercises below will help you to do this.

 Releasing the larynx
Produce a hollow 'ghur' sound, either speaking or on a pitch of your choice. Raise the back of your tongue against your soft palate so the 'g' is produced at the back of the throat. (If you are unsure where your soft palate is, roll your tongue back along the roof of the mouth from behind your teeth. With the tip of your tongue you will first feel the bony hard palate and then the fleshy soft palate.) Watch this in a mirror. The hollow vowel which follows should make your larynx drop dramatically.

During this exercise, if you are producing a hollow sound (like a sea lion!) you have successfully used a muscle called the *sterno-thyroid* to pull the larynx down from underneath, rather than using the hyoid bone to force the larynx down from above.

 Begin the exercise below at a comfortable pitch for you, but near the bottom of your range. Repeat several times using the 'ghur' sound. Once you have mastered this, move onto a gentle, continuous 'vvv' sound.

Next, repeat the exercise using a hollow humming. Let a little air escape first to create space at the back of the throat and neck. Whilst producing the 'vvv' sound or when humming, the larynx should stay reasonably low.

 Lowering the larynx to produce a dark tone
Try the following exercise, based on the 'ghur' exercise above. Again, choose a fairly low starting pitch. This time, join the 'ghur' onto an 'oo'. The 'ghur' will lower the larynx before you open onto the 'oo'. This 'oo' should be dark in tone because the larynx is low, the throat is open and, therefore, the vocal tract is lengthened. Some people like this darker sound. It can be useful in sombre pieces such as Rimsky-Korsakov's *Our Father* or the 'Lacrymosa' from Mozart's *Requiem*.

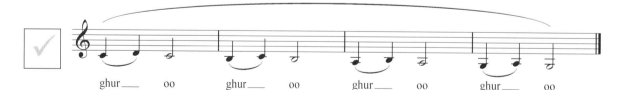

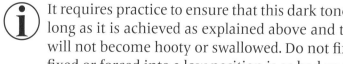

 It requires practice to ensure that this dark tone does not become hard or shallow. As long as it is achieved as explained above and the hyoid bone is not pushed down, it will not become hooty or swallowed. Do not fix the larynx down – a larynx which is fixed or forced into a low position is as bad as one which is too fixed too high. If you have any doubts about any of this, talk to your choir trainer or singing teacher.

Producing a bright tone

While you may want to use a dark tone on occasions, you should normally aim to produce a resonant, bright sound. Brightness aids good intonation and enables the natural clarity and energy of your voice to emerge. To achieve this you need to remain relaxed and focused. On this page and the next are a few tips to help you.

Relaxing your throat and jaw

Aim to sing with a relaxed throat and jaw at all times. If you find your throat is tight when you sing, try these exercises to help widen and relax your throat:

Try laughing heartily – a real belly-laugh – without making a sound. Imagine you want to laugh, but are in a place where you must not make a sound. Do you feel a widening in the throat? A silent sob or cry has the same effect. You should feel a release of tension, not a stretch.

This may feel tricky at first, but persist. You are learning to harness what is usually an involuntary emotional and physical response, during which the throat naturally widens. It is part of providing support around the voice and will help ensure that you always sing with a full, open tone.

The next exercise helps to widen the throat by making you tap into the same natural reflex action described above. You may find it easier to approach throat-widening from the perspective of this exercise. Choose a comfortable starting note.

This exercise is based on the 'Placing the voice in neutral' exercise on page 6, but this time you vocalize on the outward movement and inhale at every rest.

Singing with a nasal tone

One barrier to a full, bright sound is singing with a nasal tone. This is a common problem, as singers are often tempted to constrict the throat and direct the sound down the nose when trying to reach higher notes. However, a nasal tone is not pleasant to listen to. It is also much harder to produce sound when singing down the nose because the effort is divided in two (between the nose and the mouth). This requires extra breath pressure and in turn, causes tightening of the throat. This may lead to physical problems with the voice.

It is not always easy to know if you are doing this. Your choir trainer may point it out, but there are a few ways of checking for yourself. One common sign is tickling in the throat after you have been singing high in your range.

To identify what a nasal tone sounds and feels like, sing the sound 'ng' (like the end of the word 'sing') on any comfortable note. Notice how, when you do this, the tongue is raised and the soft palate lowered. All the sound is directed down the nose. Pinch your nose, and the sound will stop.

Now sing 'ah' instead, and then pinch your nose. Does the sound change at all? If so, you are producing a nasal sound when you sing. The exercises overleaf will help you to eliminate this problem and produce a full, bright tone.

Eliminating a nasal tone

Choosing any comfortable note, sing 'ng' and then move without a break to 'ah'. You should be using the elevated tongue position described in 'Releasing the larynx' on page 10. The soft palate has to be raised up from the tongue to let the sound travel forward to the mouth. Try pinching your nose now. If you have lifted the soft palate efficiently, the sound should not change.

If you find this exercise tricky, try using a hard 'g' between the 'ng' sound and the 'ah'. Place the 'g' on the hard palate so that the sound equates to 'ngGah'. The hard 'g' should throw the sound forward.

To help with this, try the following exercise. Choose a starting pitch comfortable for you, and move the starting pitch up or down a semitone with each repetition. Concentrate on singing with the sound at the front of the mouth, not coming down the nose.

Raising the soft palate

Choose a starting pitch comfortable for you, and move the starting pitch up or down a semitone with each repetition. Make the 'b' sound at the end of each note energetic and prominent. Again, make sure you bring the sound to the front of your mouth.

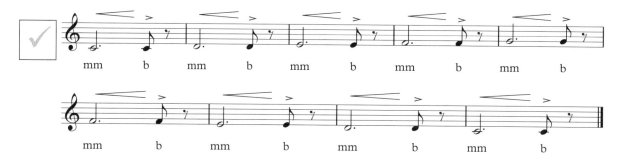

WHAT SINGERS SAY

'By slowly cutting out the nasality in the sound and by reducing breath pressure, an easier, more balanced sound began to emerge in my voice.' Nicholas, aged 28

'Something I've learned is that my whole body has to be involved in my singing. If my posture isn't good, I can't use my back to support the sound. Doing so means that pressure is removed from my larynx and the resulting sound is not only freer and bigger but much easier to produce.' Lois, aged 22

VOICE CARE TIP

To improve your posture, consider learning Alexander Technique. This teaches people to be aware of their bodies and helps to set up good posture habits.

Alternatively, you could learn Pilates (say 'Pee - lah - tees'). This aims to change the way you move and how you align your body. As well as improving posture, it can help your strength and muscle tone, your respiratory system, the mobility of your joints and your immune system.

The word *falsetto* comes from the Italian word *falso*, meaning 'false'. This implies that the falsetto sound is unnatural; however, it is an essential part of every voice. In both men and women, it is rather like the sound made by the young voice before puberty (the larynx changes slightly at puberty, altering the sound of the voice).

In men, falsetto is easy to hear because it is different from the usual or 'full' voice. Women and children also have a falsetto voice, but it tends to be slightly breathy and difficult to project. It is not particularly useful for women or children to exercise their falsetto range, but it is very useful for men, as it can improve the tone in their full voice, particularly the higher register. For tenors, using falsetto is important while their voices are developing. The following exercises are for men only.

Accessing the falsetto voice

Experiment with high notes to find your falsetto voice (ask your choir trainer or teacher to help you with this). Having located the sound, sing the following exercise with your falsetto voice. Choose a comfortable starting note.

etc.

wah wah wah wah wah wah wah wah wah wah wah wah wah wah wah wah

Repeat this exercise using the five pure vowels listed in the Diction section (page 14).

Producing the correct falsetto sound

When singing falsetto, the sound should be gentle and not harsh. If the sound is strangled, it is because the larynx is being pulled up by the wrong muscles in the jaw. The movement of the hyoid bone and larynx should not be restricted (see pages 9 and 10). If your sound is gentle and rounder, you will notice a slight upwards movement of the hyoid bone and larynx, but there will be no tension.

The sound may be weak and rather breathy at first, but with practice it will become stronger and more efficient. (Listening to a recording of your falsetto voice can be helpful until you are accustomed to the sound and how it feels.) It is important to get the correct, released sound, as this will help to provide space above the larynx and in the throat. Don't allow the muscles to restrict or squash the larynx in any way.

Avoiding a strangled sound

If your falsetto produces a strangled sound, try the following. Repeat the exercise shown above. This time, precede each vowel with a 'b' (e.g. bah, bah). Next, repeat the exercise using a rolled 'r' (e.g. rah, rah). You could also combine these to create a 'brrr' sound to precede each vowel.

Also, practise the 'Releasing the larynx' exercises on pages 10. This will help you make a free sound without allowing tension in your voice.

PRACTICE TIP

Always listen to yourself critically to ensure that you are making the correct sound. What you hear when you sing or speak is different from what another person hears (you will have noticed this when hearing a recording of yourself speaking). By recording yourself singing, you can hear things that are good, and things that need improvement. If you do this regularly, you will hear how your voice improves over time.

Diction

When you sing, your aim is to communicate the words and the music to your listeners. Vowels and consonants are the tools that you use to do this. In each piece that you sing, they should be used and adapted to create the appropriate style, give conviction to the performance and bring the music to life.

Working on **diction** – the correct production of vowels and consonants – helps you to develop a full range of tone and to sing texts with greater expression, meaning and clarity.

Vowels

Here is a list of words containing five different vowel sounds. Practise these vowels regularly with your usual vocal exercises. Producing good vowel sounds will enable you to develop a resonant and bright tone. This will make the sound project and will help your tuning.

Ee	as in	me
Eh	as in	leg
Ah	as in	father
Aw	as in	door
Oo	as in	moon

Consonants

Your consonants need to be clear, without interrupting the line of the music. Think of them as being added within a melody to energize the vowels. The following exercise can help you to achieve the right balance of clear consonants and smooth lines.

Clear consonants and smooth lines

Choose a phrase which has lots of consonants, or one which you find difficult. Sing the phrase with a single vowel sound throughout. Repeat this until you can achieve a smooth line. Then add the words, but aim to keep the line as smooth as when you sang it with just the vowel sound.

Moving between vowels and consonants

Remember that the vowel provides the sustained sound and the consonants add the punctuation. So, when a vowel follows a consonant, the vowel needs to be formed quickly. When the mouth opens to produce the vowel, the tongue should be prepared and shaped immediately to produce a resonant sound.

When a consonant follows a vowel, aim to keep the resonant vowel sound for as long as possible, and move the mouth and tongue to form the final consonant quickly. In this way, consonants do not interrupt the line of the melody (which is produced by the vowel sounds).

Use the words in the box, or your own list of words which have consonants at the beginning and the end. Practise singing each of these words on one note in your chest register. Make the consonants short and the vowels long. How resonant can you make each vowel?

Loop		L	oo	p
Need		N	ee	d
Blend		Bl	eh	nd
Lark		L	ah	k
Lord		L	aw	d

WHAT SINGERS SAY

'I've had Alexander Technique lessons every week for the last 4 years in term time and I have noticed a huge difference in the way I hold myself to sing. It enables all my muscles to be free and work to their optimum.' Jane, aged 17

Strength of consonants

Using the list of words above or some of your own, try these experiments with consonants. (Remember to keep the vowels resonant.) Sing each word:

- quietly, with the consonants clear but not very loud.

- quietly, with the consonants as loud as you can.

- loudly, with the consonants clear but not loud.

- loudly, with the consonants as loud as you can.

Starting notes with a vowel

There are three ways of starting a note with a vowel sound: aspirated onset, glottal onset (or glottal stop) and simultaneous onset. Try each of these methods so you know what they feel and sound like, using the exercises below.

Aspirated onset

Choose a note in the middle of your range and sing 'ah', starting the sound with a long 'h' (this is called an **aspirate**). In other words, sing 'hah'. When you do this, the air starts moving first, then the vocal folds vibrate to produce the 'ah' sound.

Glottal onset (or **glottal stop**)

Using the same note, sing 'ah'. Begin the sound with a hard attack (as you might use to emphasize the first letter of the word *arm*). This time, you started the sound with your vocal folds together; the vocal folds moved first and then the air was passed over them.

Simultaneous onset

Now try to sing 'ah' without an aspirate or a glottal attack. This time, the air and the vocal folds will start moving at the same time. Be critical of your sound. It may take practice to be able to produce a simultaneous onset.

Normally, you should aim to produce a simultaneous onset to each note. If you use too many aspirated onsets, your voice will sound breathy; too many glottal onsets and your voice will stick out. The exercise below will help you to improve your control of the start of notes so that you can produce the simultaneous onset more easily.

Choose a comfortable starting note. Practise this exercise, trying not to attack the beginning of each note too strongly. Aim to reach a point where you can sing the vowel 'ah' cleanly and in tune without an attack. Then continue by trying this with different vowels on other notes in your range. Sing some loudly and some softly.

Tick the box when you have tried all the exercises on this page.

WHAT SINGERS SAY

'I had serious back problems which began when I was at university. Through physiotherapy and Pilates I have been able to stop the problems from recurring. Now my body is stronger and supports my voice better – and I know how to sing without allowing tension to creep in. I no longer find that all the muscles ache after a long concert or rehearsal. I just wish I had known about Pilates years ago, and understood what a profound effect posture could have on my whole body as well as my singing voice!' Andrea, aged 26

Diphthongs

A **diphthong** is two vowel sounds which are pronounced as one syllable. For example, the word 'day' contains the vowel sounds 'eh' and 'ee'. When this word is spoken, the tongue moves quickly from one sound to the next.

When singing a diphthong, consider how to treat the individual vowel sounds. Imagine the diphthong is to be sung on a long note. Should each vowel sound be equal in length, or should one be longer than the other?

Usually, when singing a diphthong, the first vowel sound should be as long as possible. The second vowel sound should be placed as late as possible, as long as it is clear and does not delay the vowel or consonant which follows it.

Experimenting with diphthongs

- Sing the word 'day'. First, sing it so that each vowel sound lasts an equal length of time (as in bar 1, below).

- Then sing it so that the first vowel sound is very short and the second is as long as possible (as in bar 2).

- Finally, sing the word again, making the first vowel sound as long as possible, changing to the second vowel sound as close to the end of the note as possible (as in bar 3).

The version in bar 3 is what you should normally aim to achieve in your singing. Practise this using other words containing diphthongs, for example, 'sound' or 'main'.

Diction tips

- Sometimes it is necessary to shorten a note to create time to breathe and ensure that the next word starts cleanly, without sounding rushed. When you do this, be careful to place the final consonant of the word together with the other singers.

- The relationship between the volume of consonants and the volume of vowels depends on the style of music. Listen to a recording of yourself. Does the volume of vowels and consonants sound right? If you are not sure, ask your choir trainer.

- When deciding on the style of your diction, think about the room where you will be singing. The size, shape and contents of a room can alter its acoustic characteristics. If you can, practise in the room or listen to other performers to hear how the acoustics change. You can then adjust your diction as necessary and settle into a performance quickly.

PRACTICE TIP

How often you practise is just as important as how long you practise for. Even a short daily session keeps your voice and muscles in good condition. If you don't have time for a long session every day, do a few warm-ups and basic exercises, wherever you are. If you do this, your longer practice sessions will be more productive when you have time for them, as your voice will still be in good shape.

For your Yellow performance targets, you will be expected to sing:

- Three contrasting solo pieces with a range of over an octave. These should be sung from memory.

- A solo or solo line in a concert or service (selected and prepared in advance).

With your choir trainer, choose the pieces and the solo you will sing, and arrange where and when you will sing them.

 Write the names of your three pieces here:

When and where will you be performing these pieces?

Write the name of your solo here:

When and where will you be performing this?

 Preparing for your performance

When you perform, your choir trainer will be listening for the following:

- Clear articulation and projection

- Even and resonant tone throughout your range

- The ability to move smoothly and with agility between the different registers of the voice

- Good breath control demonstrated through dynamics, a focused tone throughout the dynamic range, and good intonation

- The use of different vocal colours (see pages 10 and 11)

To prepare your pieces and solo:

- Practise at home. If you know the music very well, you will be more confident in your performance.

- Sing the tune to 'ah' or hum it until you are confident of where it goes and how it feels in your voice.

- Practise your pieces without accompaniment. This will help you to learn all the notes accurately.

- Practise sliding between each note to get a sense of smoothness. This will help you to connect the notes.

Performance

 Listen carefully to yourself as you practise. Ask yourself the following questions:

- Have I learnt all the notes accurately?
- What are the words trying to communicate?
- Am I making all the words clear?
- Am I singing with clear consonants, while keeping the melody smooth?
- Is my diction appropriate for the style of music I am singing?
- Is my tuning good?
- Is my breathing good?
- Is my throat staying relaxed?

- Am I breathing in the appropriate places?
- Am I using contrasting dynamics?
- Is the sound still focused when I sing quietly?
- Will I be heard by someone at the back of the room where I will be performing?
- Is my music held at the right height?
- Is my posture relaxed but stable?
- Do I look like a confident performer?

 Planning for the performance
Who is accompanying you? Do they need a copy of the music to play from? Make sure you have a copy for them, and one for you if necessary.

What will you wear for the performance? If you do not have a choir uniform and are allowed to choose your performance clothes, it is best to try on your chosen outfit before the final performance to make sure that it is comfortable to sing in.

Make sure that your clothes are not too tight as this will restrict your breathing. Also, make sure that the heels of your shoes are not too high, otherwise your knees and legs will become tense and this will restrict your breathing. Whatever you choose to wear, make sure you feel comfortable and look right for the occasion.

 Unaccompanied singing
If any of your performance is unaccompanied, your choir trainer will want to know that you can keep going with confidence. Keep the rhythm strong and steady, and try not to speed up or slow down. Concentrate on staying at the right pitch. It helps if you know the tune really well, because you will be sure about the exact size of each interval.

 After your performance
When you have finished your performance, your choir trainer will give you feedback about aspects of your singing. He or she may feel you need to continue working on one particular aspect of your voice and to perform again later. If so, keep practising the exercises in this book and the others that your choir trainer will introduce during rehearsals, and you will find that your singing improves.

 VOICE CARE TIP
Many singers cough and clear their throats before singing, but this actually closes the throat. Instead, bring water to rehearsals, as swallowing will clear away any excess mucus. Try not to clear your throat every time you are about to begin singing.

Here are some new key signatures:

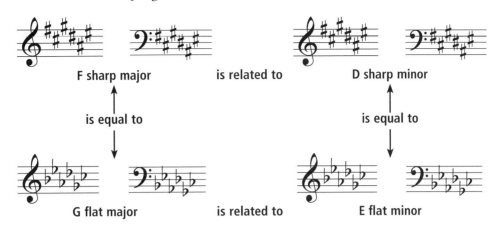

Sing the scales and arpeggios of the keys shown above.

 F sharp major and G flat major contain all of the same notes, by different names. Also, D sharp minor and E flat minor contain all of the same notes, by different names. So there are only two keys here, each with two names. The most common names used for these keys are **F sharp major** and **E flat minor**.

You now know all the major and minor keys and their key signatures. They are summarized in the chart on page 52.

 Sing the harmonic minor scale for E flat minor, then make a stairs chart for it. (For a reminder about stairs charts, see the Light Blue or Dark Blue workbooks.) On the staff, write the key signature and the notes of the scale. You will need an accidental – think carefully!

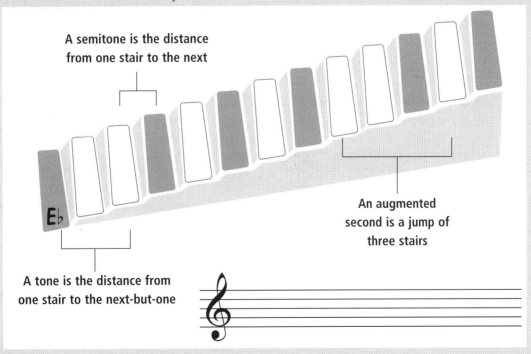

A semitone is the distance from one stair to the next

An augmented second is a jump of three stairs

A tone is the distance from one stair to the next-but-one

 In the key of F sharp major, which note is *not* a sharp?

New keys and key signatures

Name the six flats in the key signature of E flat minor.

____ flat   ____ flat

____ flat   ____ flat

What is the relative major of this key?

____ flat   ____ flat

What is the key signature of B minor?

____ sharp(s) ____ flat(s)

Can you link these keys in order according to how many sharps their key signatures have?

Circle the key with the most sharps. What is its relative minor?

D major

F♯ minor   A minor

G major   E major

Put a clef on this staff and then write the key signature of D flat major.

What is the name of the other key which shares this key signature?

_____ minor

Which two keys have this key signature?

_____ major and _____ minor

Finish this pattern:

F   B♭   E♭   ____ ____ ____

...and this one:

G   D   A   ____ ____ ____

Need a clue? Think about the interval between each note in the pattern, or about the key signatures of their major keys. If you need help with these questions, ask your choir trainer or look at the chart on page 52.

The **melodic minor scale** is different from the harmonic minor scale you have already learned. In a melodic minor scale, the sixth and seventh notes change depending on whether the scale is ascending (going up) or descending (going down).

Ascending, both the sixth and the seventh notes of the scale are a semitone higher than they are in the key signature. They are shown by accidentals in the music.

Scale of A melodic minor, ascending

 Sing this scale. Then sing a scale of A harmonic minor. Can you hear that in each of these scales, the sixth note is different? (You may need to sing a few times.)

 Make a stairs chart for D melodic minor, ascending. Fill in the notes on the staff too. Put the key signature after the clef, and remember you will need to add accidentals to the sixth and seventh notes as well.

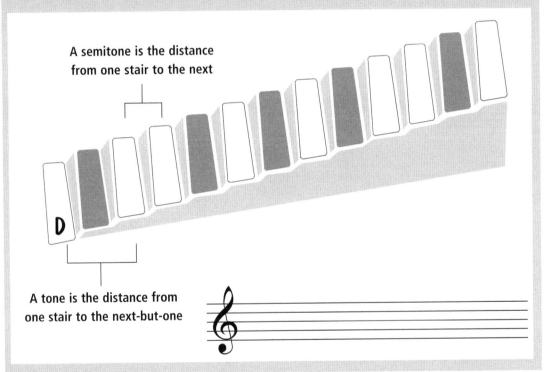

A semitone is the distance from one stair to the next

A tone is the distance from one stair to the next-but-one

 In an ascending melodic minor scale, the sixth and seventh notes are sharpened. In a descending melodic minor scale, these notes are not sharpened. The melodic minor scale going down uses exactly the same notes as its relative major. Therefore, it has the same sharps or flats that are shown in its key signature.

Scale of A melodic minor, descending

 The key signature of A minor has no sharps or flats, so there are no sharps or flats in the descending melodic minor scale. However in written music you may see accidentals to cancel any sharp or flat signs used on the way up the scale.

Make a stairs chart for D melodic minor, descending. Fill in the notes on the staff too. Remember to put the key signature after the clef.

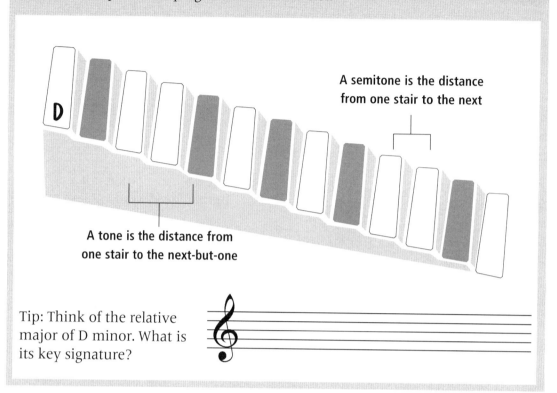

A semitone is the distance from one stair to the next

A tone is the distance from one stair to the next-but-one

Tip: Think of the relative major of D minor. What is its key signature?

Sing some melodic minor scales, up and down. Then sing some harmonic minor scales, to compare the different kinds of minor scale.

What is the name of the seventh note in the scale of E melodic minor, ascending?

What is the interval between this note and the E above it?

What is the name of the note below E in the scale of E melodic minor, descending?

What is the interval between this note and the E above it?

Compare the scale of A melodic minor going up with the scale of A major. One note is in A major but not in A minor. Which is it?

Where does this note come in the scale? Circle the correct answer.

1st 2nd 3rd 4th 5th 6th 7th

Double sharps and double flats

(i) This sign is a **double sharp**. It means that the note following it is made two semitones higher.

×

Double sharp

♭♭

Double flat

This sign is a **double flat.** It means that the note following it is made two semitones lower.

F double sharp is two semitones higher than F – so it is the same pitch as G.

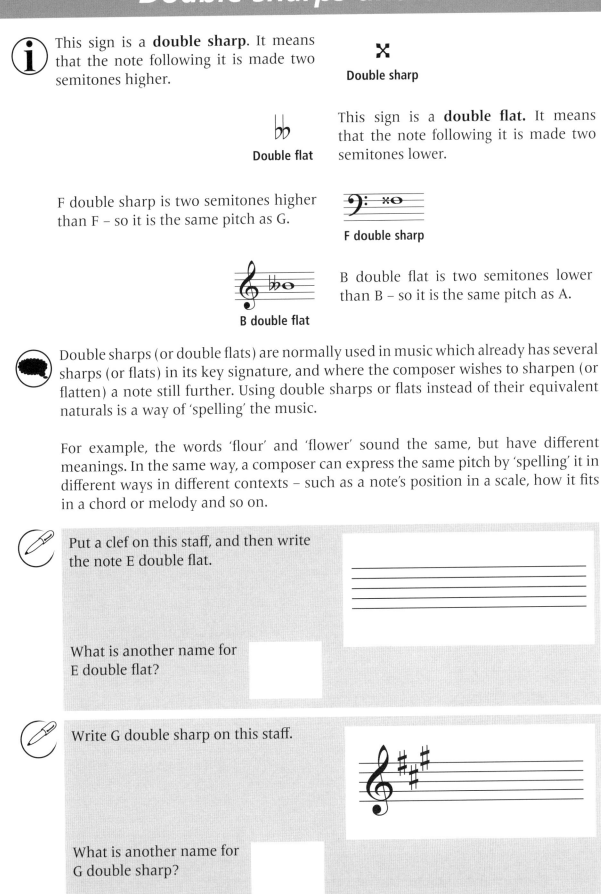

F double sharp

B double flat

B double flat is two semitones lower than B – so it is the same pitch as A.

Double sharps (or double flats) are normally used in music which already has several sharps (or flats) in its key signature, and where the composer wishes to sharpen (or flatten) a note still further. Using double sharps or flats instead of their equivalent naturals is a way of 'spelling' the music.

For example, the words 'flour' and 'flower' sound the same, but have different meanings. In the same way, a composer can express the same pitch by 'spelling' it in different ways in different contexts – such as a note's position in a scale, how it fits in a chord or melody and so on.

Put a clef on this staff, and then write the note E double flat.

What is another name for E double flat?

Write G double sharp on this staff.

What is another name for G double sharp?

How many semitones are there between G double sharp and B natural?

Double sharps and double flats

ℹ️ Just like a sharp or a flat, a double sharp or a double flat lasts until the next barline or until it is cancelled.

A natural sign in front of a note following a double sharp or double flat means that the note becomes a natural.

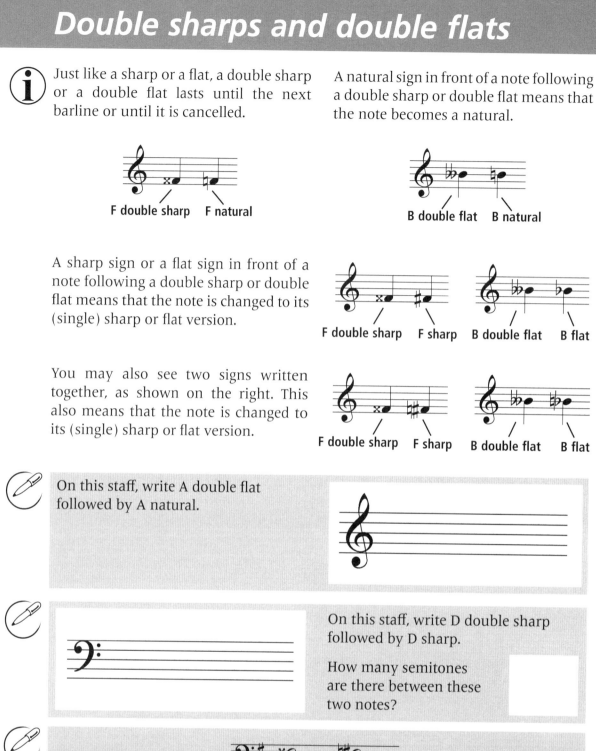

A sharp sign or a flat sign in front of a note following a double sharp or double flat means that the note is changed to its (single) sharp or flat version.

You may also see two signs written together, as shown on the right. This also means that the note is changed to its (single) sharp or flat version.

🖊️ On this staff, write A double flat followed by A natural.

🖊️ On this staff, write D double sharp followed by D sharp.

How many semitones are there between these two notes?

🖊️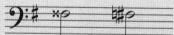

Name the first note on the staff above.

What is the name of the second note?

Write the note A on the top line of the staff on the right. Put a symbol in front of it to make it the same pitch as the first note above.

An **augmented** interval is an interval to which an extra semitone has been added. (Augmented means 'made bigger'.) For example, an augmented fourth is a perfect fourth plus one semitone.

Perfect fourth

An augmented fourth is one semitone larger than a perfect fourth.

Augmented fourth

 A **diminished** interval is an interval from which a semitone has been taken away. (Diminished means 'made smaller'.) For example, a diminished fifth is a perfect fifth minus one semitone.

Perfect fifth

A diminished fifth is one semitone smaller than a perfect fifth.

Diminished fifth

 Sing these intervals.

 An **augmented fourth** sounds the same as a **diminished fifth**. Its size is *between* a perfect fourth and a perfect fifth. It is also known as a **tritone**, because it is the same size as three tones added together.

 The same interval can be written down in different ways. Writing an interval as an augmented fourth rather than a diminished fifth (or vice versa) is another way that a composer uses of 'spelling' the music. The way that the composer chooses to express an interval can depend on its context – for example, the harmony that comes before or after the interval, or what happens next in the melody.

 Link these intervals in order of size. Start with *either* the largest *or* the smallest.

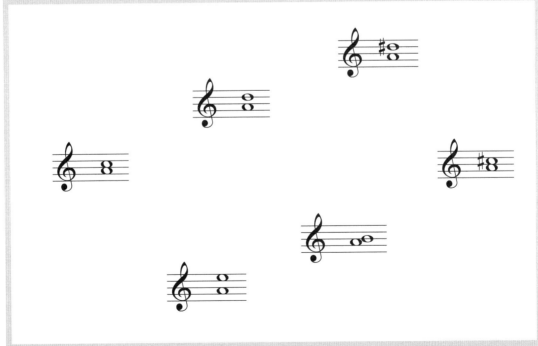

One of these intervals is an augmented fourth. Draw a circle around this interval.

On this staff, write a note which is a minor second above the one shown.

How many semitones are there between these notes?

On this staff, write the note a diminished fifth above the one shown.

How many semitones are there between these notes?

Link the six intervals below in order of size. Start with the largest *or* the smallest.

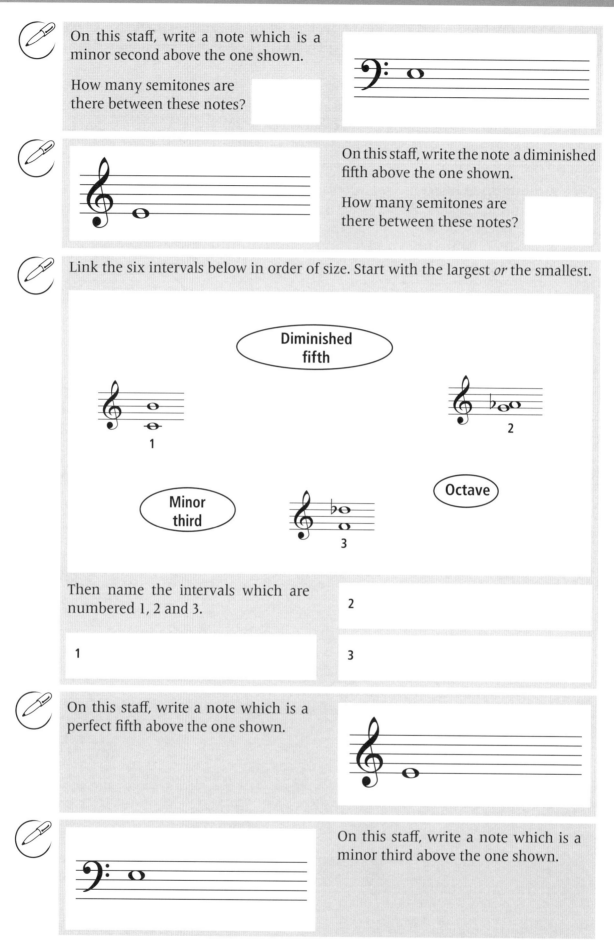

Diminished fifth

1

2

Minor third

3

Octave

Then name the intervals which are numbered 1, 2 and 3.

1

2

3

On this staff, write a note which is a perfect fifth above the one shown.

On this staff, write a note which is a minor third above the one shown.

If you need help with these intervals, ask your choir trainer.

The tonic chord

The tonic chord (or tonic triad) is a major triad based on the tonic (or key note) of a key. The note which a triad is based on is called its **root**. The other two notes in a major triad are intervals of a third and a fifth above the root. They are called the **third** and the **fifth** of the triad.

For example, in the key of G major, the tonic chord is based on G, so it contains the notes G, B and D.

The tonic chord (tonic triad) in the key of G major

The dominant chord

Counting the tonic as one, count up the scale to the fifth note. This note is called the **dominant**. A triad based on the dominant note is called the dominant chord (or dominant triad). The dominant note is the root of the triad. The other two notes are a third and a fifth above this root note.

In G major, the dominant (fifth note of the scale) is D. So the dominant chord is made up of D, F sharp and A.

The dominant chord (or dominant triad) in the key of G major

The subdominant chord

The fourth note of a scale is called its **subdominant**. In G major, this note is C. The subdominant note is the root of the subdominant chord (or subdominant triad).

In G major, the subdominant chord contains the notes C, E and G.

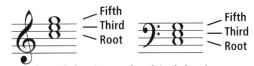

The subdominant chord (subdominant triad) in the key of G major

The name of a chord depends on the key. In G major, D is the dominant. But in A major, D is the subdominant.

The tonic chord, the dominant chord and the subdominant chord are known as the **primary chords** of a key. They are called 'primary' because they are the ones most often used in many types of music for the harmony that goes with a melody. Many pieces of music use only the three primary chords in their harmony.

With your choir, think of some traditional folk tunes, nursery rhymes and contemporary pop tunes, and ask your choir trainer to play the chords that go with them. Sing the tunes along with the chords. You will find that many of the tunes use only, or mainly, their primary chords.

In this box, write the names of some well-known songs or tunes which use only primary chords in their harmony.

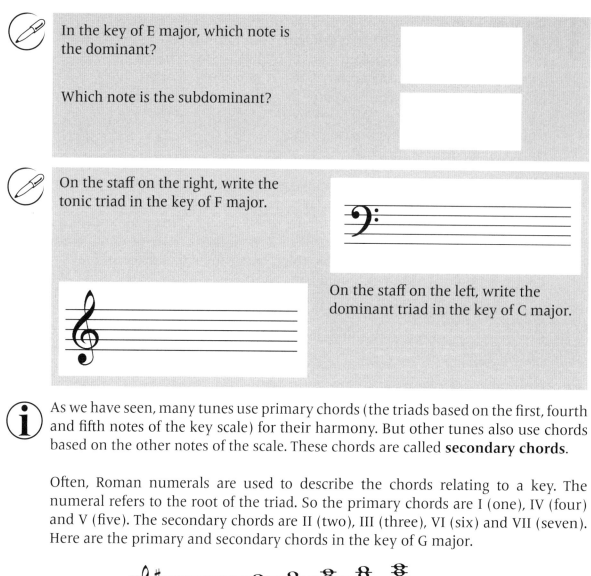

In the key of E major, which note is the dominant?

Which note is the subdominant?

On the staff on the right, write the tonic triad in the key of F major.

On the staff on the left, write the dominant triad in the key of C major.

(i) As we have seen, many tunes use primary chords (the triads based on the first, fourth and fifth notes of the key scale) for their harmony. But other tunes also use chords based on the other notes of the scale. These chords are called **secondary chords**.

Often, Roman numerals are used to describe the chords relating to a key. The numeral refers to the root of the triad. So the primary chords are I (one), IV (four) and V (five). The secondary chords are II (two), III (three), VI (six) and VII (seven). Here are the primary and secondary chords in the key of G major.

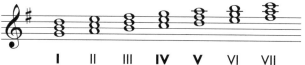

I   II   III   **IV**   **V**   VI   VII

The primary chords are numbered in **bold** type

Look at the chord on the right, and answer the questions below to describe it in different keys:

In the key of A minor, what is the name of this chord?

What is the name of this chord in C major? (Use a Roman numeral.)

What is the name of this chord in E minor? (Use both a Roman numeral and a chord name.)

If you need help with these triads, ask your choir trainer.

(i) If a chord has the root at the bottom, we say it is in **root position**. It doesn't matter how many notes are in the chord, whether any notes are used twice, whether the notes are high or low, or which note is at the top. Here is a C major triad:

If a chord has the third at the bottom, it is in **first inversion**. If it has its fifth at the bottom, it is in **second inversion**.

In root position
(root at the bottom)

In first inversion
(third at the bottom)

In second inversion
(fifth at the bottom)

(i) The notes of a chord can be arranged in many different ways. The arrangement of notes in chords is called **voicing.** The E minor chords below are both in root position, but they have different voicings.

The notes can be **doubled** (used twice at different octaves). In this example, the root is doubled at the top and bottom of the chord.

— Root
— Third

— Fifth
— Root

The notes can be spread out. In this example the root is a low bass note, the third is in the middle, and the fifth very high in the treble register. This is called **open position**. A chord where the notes are as close together as possible is in **close** or **closed position**.

— Fifth

— Third

— Root

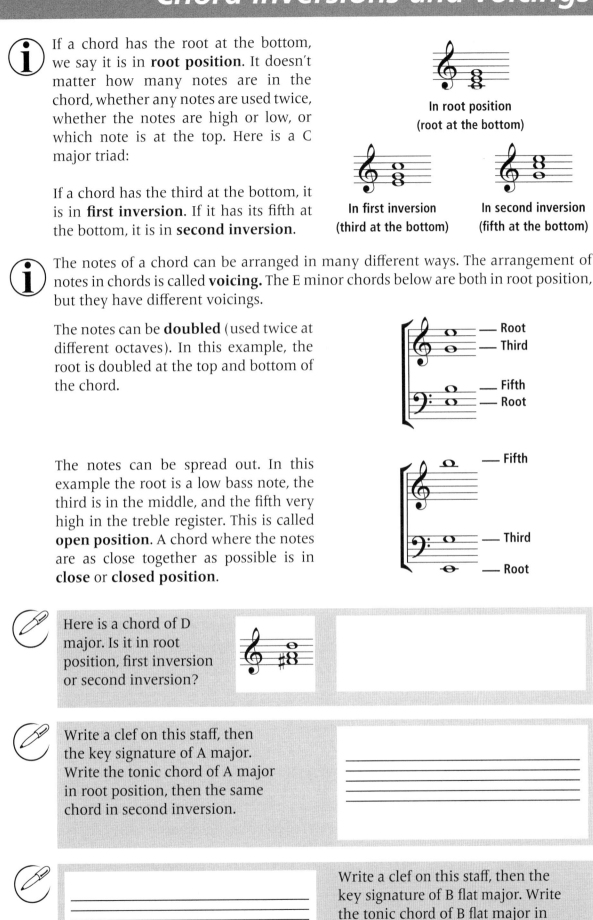

🖊 Here is a chord of D major. Is it in root position, first inversion or second inversion?

🖊 Write a clef on this staff, then the key signature of A major. Write the tonic chord of A major in root position, then the same chord in second inversion.

🖊 Write a clef on this staff, then the key signature of B flat major. Write the tonic chord of B flat major in first inversion.

Here are some chords with four notes. Play them, or ask your choir trainer to do so. They will probably sound familiar from many different styles of music.

A **dominant seventh** is the dominant triad of a key, with an added note – the minor seventh above the root. (In C major, the dominant triad is G, and the added note is F.)

Dominant seventh chord in the key of C major

This chord is a triad of C major with an added sixth (the added note is a major sixth above the root).

Chord of C major with an added sixth

Here is a triad with an added ninth (the added note is a ninth – an octave plus a major second – above the root).

Chord of C major with an added ninth

 This is the dominant chord in the key of D major. Add a seventh to the chord to make it a dominant seventh.

What is the name of this chord? (Name its root, and then decide whether the chord is major or minor.)

Here is the same chord with an added note. Is the added note a sixth, a seventh or a ninth?

 Chord symbols in written music

Sometimes written music contains symbols above or below the notes, to tell you what chords to play on a guitar or keyboard to accompany your singing. These symbols usually show the note name of the root of the triad, together with the numbers of any notes you need to add to complete the chord.

G	**Am**	**C7**	**D6**	**F9**
Play a chord of G major	Play a chord of A minor	Play C major with an added minor seventh	Play D major with an added major sixth	Play F major with an added major ninth

 Can you work out the chord symbols for the three chords at the top of this page? Write them next to the music.

A **cadence** (say 'KAY – dence') is a group of chords played one after another, like musical punctuation at the end of a phrase, section or piece. At the end of some phrases or sections, the music feels as if it needs to carry on (think of a comma in a sentence). At the end of others, it feels more finished (think of a full stop). This is partly because of the different cadences used at these points in the music.

A piece in a particular key feels 'finished' when it ends on the tonic (chord I). It feels most finished if the chord *before* the tonic is the dominant (chord V). This is called a **perfect cadence.** If a section ends on the dominant chord, the music feels incomplete, as if it needs to carry on. A cadence with the dominant as its final chord is called an **imperfect cadence.** Any chord can precede the dominant in an imperfect cadence – the most common are the tonic or subdominant (chord IV).

Perfect cadence

V — I
Dominant — Tonic

Imperfect cadence

I — V
Tonic — Dominant

Imperfect cadence

IV — V
Subdominant — Dominant

A **plagal cadence** ends on the tonic, but is preceded by the subdominant (chord IV). In an **interrupted cadence**, the dominant (chord V) implies the tonic will follow, but the relative minor (chord VI, also called the **submediant**) follows instead. This makes the music seem to 'swerve' away from the tonic.

Plagal cadence

IV — I
Subdominant — Tonic

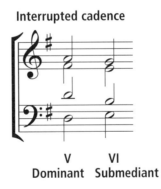

Interrupted cadence

V — VI
Dominant — Submediant

All these examples are in G major. Ask your choir trainer to play these cadences (and some in other keys too) and see if you can identify the different types.

 Look at the three cadences below and identify what type they are, and in what key. Look carefully at the key signatures!

These time signatures work in the same way as the other time signatures that you know. The top number tells you how many beats are in each bar. The bottom number tells you what kind of beats they are.

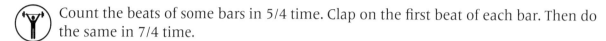

| 5 crotchet beats in a bar | 5 quaver beats in a bar | 7 crotchet beats in a bar | 7 quaver beats in a bar |

Count the beats of some bars in 5/4 time. Clap on the first beat of each bar. Then do the same in 7/4 time.

Music with five beats in a bar often feels as if the beats are grouped in twos and threes. You may be able to hear a group of two followed by a group of three, or a group of three then a group of two.

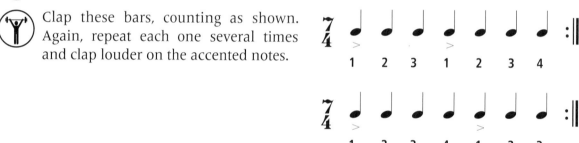

Clap the bars on the right while counting as shown. Repeat each one several times. Clap louder on the notes which have accents, feeling the different groups of two and three.

Music with seven beats in a bar can also have smaller groups of beats within each bar. Sometimes the beats are grouped as three followed by four, or four followed by three.

Clap these bars, counting as shown. Again, repeat each one several times and clap louder on the accented notes.

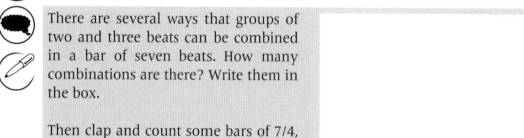

Music with seven beats in a bar can also be grouped in twos and threes. This time, of course, there will be three groups within each bar.

There are several ways that groups of two and three beats can be combined in a bar of seven beats. How many combinations are there? Write them in the box.

Then clap and count some bars of 7/4, grouping the beats in the different ways that you have written.

If you know any music which has any of the time signatures on this page, sing it with your choir. If not, listen to a recording. Ask your choir trainer for suggestions.

While you sing or listen, count the beats in your head. Are the beats within each bar grouped? If so, are they grouped in twos, threes or fours?

Some music is not in a major or minor key, but based on special scales called **modes**. There are several different modes. Each has its own pattern of tones and semitones which give it its own sound. Modal music sounds neither strictly major nor minor.

 Some early church music, called plainchant or plainsong, is written in modes, as are many traditional songs. If you know any music in these styles, sing it with your choir. If not, listen to a recording. Ask your choir trainer for suggestions.

 Here are five of the most common modes, with their interval patterns of tones (shown with a **T**) and semitones (shown with an **S**). You can play them on the white keys of a keyboard, and this is how they are shown below. But a mode can start on any note as long as the interval pattern of tones and semitones is correct.

The *Dorian* mode has the same interval pattern as the white notes on a keyboard from D to D.

The *Phrygian* mode has the same interval pattern as the white notes on a keyboard from E to E.

The *Lydian* mode has the same interval pattern as the white notes on a keyboard from F to F.

The *Mixolydian* mode has the same interval pattern as the white notes on a keyboard from G to G.

The *Aeolian* mode has the same interval pattern as the white notes on a keyboard from A to A.

 Sing or play these modes, up and down an octave. Listen to their different sounds.

 In the treble clef, write one octave of a Dorian mode, starting on C. You will need some accidentals.

In the bass clef, write one octave of a Phrygian mode, starting on A. You will need some accidentals.

Performance directions

 You will find many kinds of instructions in your printed music that give you clues as to how it should be sung. These instructions are usually in Italian. Sometimes they are shortened versions of Italian words. Here are some general instructions:

assai (say 'a – sigh')	very
quasi (say 'kwah – zee')	as if, almost
poco a poco	little by little
prima, primo (say 'pree – ma/moh')	first
seconda, secondo	second
sopra	above
sotto	below, under
simile (or ***sim.***) (say 'si – mi – ley')	continue in the same way
col, colla, con	with
senza	without
non	not
ma non troppo	but not too much
tacet (say 'tasset')	silent (often used to tell you not to sing in a particular section of music)

 These instructions tell you about the character of the music:

animato (say 'anny – mah –toh')	animated, lively
scherzo (say 'skairt – soh')	a joke or humorous piece
con anima	with feeling, soul or spirit
appassionato	passionately
delicato	delicately
ritmico	rhythmically
agitato (say 'aji – tah – toh')	agitated
energico	energetically
tranquillo (say 'tran – kee – loh')	calmly
dolente (say 'do – len – tey')	sadly, mournfully
triste (say 'tris – tey')	sadly, sorrowfully
grave (say 'gra – vey')	slow and solemn
grandioso	grandly
furioso	furiously
deciso (say 'de – chee – zoh')	decisively
con brio (say 'con bree – oh')	with vigour

These instructions tell you how the voice should sound:

marcato (say 'mar – kah – toh')	marked, accented
leggiero (say 'lej – ee – air – oh')	lightly
pesante (say 'pe – zan – teh')	heavily
risoluto (say 'riz – oh – loo – toh')	bold, strong
voce (say 'vo – cheh')	voice
sotto voce	in an undertone
sonoro	resonant, with a rich tone

 These instructions tell you about the general sound of the music:

perdendosi	dying away
morendo	dying away
calando	getting quieter, dying away
smorzando (say 'smor – tsan – doh')	dying away in tone and speed
niente (say 'nyen – tey')	nothing (no sound)
lunga pausa (say 'pow–zuh')	long pause

Find the composer

Write the Italian words for the terms given below into the boxes. If you get them right, the letters in the shaded boxes will spell the name of a choral composer.

1) Silent, don't sing

2) Slow and solemn

3) Voice

4) Heavily

5) Sadly

6) Nothing, no sound

7) Without

8) Furiously

 Sing some scales, arpeggios or vocal exercises to practise the following:

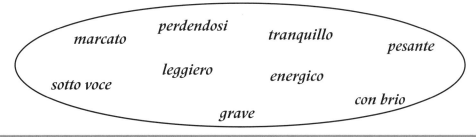

marcato   *perdendosi*   *tranquillo*   *pesante*

sotto voce   *leggiero*   *energico*   *con brio*

grave

Understanding the music we sing

 As a performer, you have to communicate the meaning of each piece you sing. To do this, you must understand the words and background of the music. For your Yellow level 'Repertoire' target (see page 49), you have to collect some information about pieces that you sing in your choir. The worksheet opposite shows the type of questions you need to answer for each piece. If you are unsure where to find out about music and composers, talk to your choir trainer.

At Yellow level you have to find out about the music and texts that you sing with your choir, and make observations about the links between the two. You are also required to show that you understand how an individual piece of music fits into the bigger picture of music history.

To achieve the target, you must show your knowledge and understanding by producing some programme notes about pieces you are working on with your choir, using some of the 'Topics for consideration' listed on page 38. You may want to listen to recordings of each piece, and of other pieces of the same style and period. You will also need to do some research, collecting information from other sources.

Here are some tips about making your research as effective as possible:

- The Internet is really useful, but may not always give you correct information. Always cross-check information in several sources.

- Keep a note of the sources you consulted in case you need to refer back to them. For example, you may want to check a fact or find an additional piece of information: it is quicker and easier to do this if you have kept a record of where you did your research.

- You may not find answers to every question about every piece of music. Gather as much information as you can.

- Make sure that you present your own work in your own words. Don't copy other people's work – you may copy their mistakes!

 Putting the information together
With your choir trainer, choose a piece that you have sung recently, or are working on currently. Answer as many of the questions on the worksheet opposite as you can. (You may want to make notes on a separate sheet too.) Make copies of the sheet so that you can repeat this exercise with other pieces of music.

Then, when you have collected the information for your piece, go to page 38 for some hints about turning the information you have collected into programme notes.

 VOICE CARE TIP
If you hold your hands behind your back when you sing, this will restrict your breathing. When singing without music, keep your hands relaxed and down by your side. This allows your rib cage to move freely.

Module C: Repertoire

Name the piece of music and the composer.

Give some biographical details of the composer (dates of birth and death, where he or she lived, nationality and so on).

What century or period was the composer writing in? Name some other composers working around the same time.

Give the key and time signature of the piece.

Where do the words come from? What language are they in? Explain briefly what they are about.

Name some other pieces by this composer.

When is the piece normally sung? At a particular time of year or for a particular event?

Give any interesting information about the composer or the piece (for example, where it was first performed).

Describe briefly how the music is put together – the number of vocal parts, the instruments involved.

What is the mood of the music?

You may photocopy this page

Writing programme notes

The main purpose of programme notes is to help the audience to understand and appreciate the music. Make your notes as interesting as possible, clear, concise and readable. Focus on the piece itself: if you include any biographical or historical information, it must be linked directly to the music.

 Write your notes on a separate piece of paper. They should be in your own words: try not to paraphrase or copy from other sources. If you want to use a quotation from a composer or writer to illustrate a certain point, keep it short. Identify it as a quotation by putting it in quotation marks, and refer to the author's name.

 Topics for consideration when writing your notes

Use the answers on the worksheet on the previous page as the basic material for your programme notes. Use the questions below to give you ideas of how to expand these answers into full, informative text. You won't want to answer all of them for every piece, but aim to produce a programme note that tells the reader about the music in an interesting and relevant way.

Discuss the themes of the text and what it communicates. What does the text describe or communicate? Does it put across a particular mood? How is this achieved?

Describe how the composer has set the words to music. Is the setting syllabic (one syllable for each note) or melismatic (one syllable over many notes)? Are any of the words repeated? Does the music highlight a particular part of the text? Does the use of the music change the mood or affect the meaning of the text in any way?

Discuss the composer's use of different colours and textures. Do many voices and instruments sing and play at once, or not? Is there particular use of contrast or dynamics? Special instrumental or vocal effects? Unusual harmonies? How do these reflect the text or affect the mood of the piece?

Think about the composer's life. Do any historical, political or personal events in the composer's life have connections with their work? Does the piece you are studying reflect this? Perhaps it reflects a particular event (e.g. the death of a family member, the crowning of a new monarch).

Think about the musical period in which the composer lived. Discuss the characteristics of music at that time. Name other pieces in the same style or genre (type of piece). Compare and contrast them with the piece you are studying. Is your piece typical of music of its period? In what way? Is there anything about your piece that is new and innovative? Did your composer influence other composers? How? Or was your composer influenced by another composer while writing this piece?

Discuss how the piece might have been performed when it was written and compare this with your performance. Are you performing the piece the way it would have been heard when it was written? Or was it written for a different combination of voices or instruments from the one you are using? Were there any special performing conventions (ways of playing or singing, for example) that would have affected the piece when it was written? If so, are you including – or excluding – any of these in your performance?

As a singer, you need to practise individually and work on your own voice and musical ability in order to improve. You may also be able to improve your skills as a choir member. At Yellow level, you are responsible within the choir for leading and looking after the less experienced singers. This is rather like being captain of a sports team; you are expected to play to the best of your ability, but you also have the added responsibility of encouraging your team members to do the best they can.

The manager of the team relies on the captain to fulfil this important job. In the same way, your choir trainer relies on you to fulfil this job within your choir. You can provide a lead to your team members by setting an example with your attendance, your singing and your behaviour in rehearsals and services or concerts.

Your choir trainer needs to know that you:

- are committed, reliable and punctual, always informing the choir trainer before being absent

- take responsibility for the less experienced singers

- understand the delicate balance in a choir between giving a strong musical lead and blending with other singers

- are an outstanding choir member, setting an excellent example to other singers (musical standards, attendance, behaviour, commitment, and so on)

- understand why it is important to participate in the practicalities of running a choir (preparing rehearsal rooms, collecting music, and so on)

 Ask yourself the following questions. Write the answers here, then ask your choir trainer to comment.

Do I set an example to other choir members? How?	
Do I help with running the choir? In what ways could I be more helpful?	
Explain the differences between solo and choral singing.	

Choir in context

 This module of *Voice for Life* is about what it means to sing in a choir and what your choir means to you and your community. The answers to these things are different for each choir and singer, so this module is tested differently from the others.

Your choir trainer will ask you to think about the topics in this section of the book and write your answers to the questions in the boxes or on separate sheets of paper. (You may be asked to work in a group with other singers.) Before you start writing, it may help to talk to other singers or do some research. To complete this module for Yellow level, you have to finish at least *one* of the topics, but your choir trainer may ask you to do more. Topic 3 is for church choirs only.

You will be given plenty of time to prepare each topic, so work through the questions carefully. Your choir trainer will look at your answers and may chat with you about them. You may be asked to follow up some points or answer more questions. When the topic is completed, he or she will sign the box in the targets on page 50.

 Topic 1: The changing repertoire of our choir
For this topic, you are required to do some research about the music your choir has sung over the years and consider what it tells you about its history. You will also think about how the choir's musical preferences and choices have changed over time and how these might influence its repertoire today and in the future.

If your choir has a long history and a lot of repertoire, you might want to concentrate on one aspect, festival, or period of time. For example you could examine what pieces have been chosen for Easter Day and how these have changed over the years, or think about the music the choir performed in its earliest days.

 How you will find out about your choir's past repertoire? Where will you look? Who will you ask? For example, you may want to look at old service sheets or music lists. Does your choir have a library? Could you talk to the librarian? Has your choir made recordings, or been reported in the local or national press? Is there an archive? In the box below, list some of the sources you plan to consult.

In the upper box on the opposite page, you will find some questions to think about when examining your choir's repertoire. Make notes of your answers on a separate sheet. You may not be able to answer all of them, and you may find information not covered by the questions that will also be useful, so make a note of that too. You may want to discuss some of the questions with your choir trainer.

Then, in the lower box, use your notes to write a repertoire report. Discuss what the repertoire history tells you about your choir, and say what new repertoire you would suggest and why. Continue on a separate sheet if necessary.

Who chose your choir's repertoire in the past? Who chooses it today? Do you help to make the choices?

How has the choir's repertoire changed over the years? What do these changes say about the choir and its audience?

Is any repertoire more popular now than in the past? Why?

Is any repertoire less popular now than in the past? Why? Should any of it be revived?

What influences your choir's repertoire selection? (Think about: the ability and tastes of the singers; the choir's role in the community; the expectations of the audience or congregation.)

If you had to suggest new repertoire for your choir, where would you look?

Suggest some new pieces for your choir. Think about why they are suitable, how the audience will react to them, and what the new pieces will say about your choir's image or status.

Repertoire report

Choir in context

Topic 2: Serving the wider community

For this topic, you are required to conceive and plan a practical event or activity to build relationships between your choir and your community. This involves thinking about how your choir already relates to the people and places around it, and what could be done to improve this. First, answer the following questions. (You may have already thought about some of these in the Module E topics at earlier levels.)

How does our choir already contribute to the community? (Consider performances, fundraising, non-musical, social, religious or pastoral activities and so on.)

Are there other ways in which the choir could contribute to the community?

Are there any special events or occasions coming up in the next year that could be a focus for the choir's contributions?

Now develop an idea for an event that your choir can organize for its community. If you want, discuss your idea with other choir or community members. It may not be possible for the event to take place, but plan it as if it were going to happen. Be practical and realistic. Think about the questions below to help you plan. Make some notes on a separate sheet, then fill in the worksheet opposite.

- What do you hope to achieve for the community?
- What do you hope to achieve for the choir?
- What tasks need to be done to make the event happen?
- What funds will you need?
- Who will take part?
- What help will you need?
- Whose permission will you need?
- How will you tell people about the project?
- How will you decide whether it has been a success?
- How will you keep a record of the event?

The worksheet will help you to draw up a detailed plan. You can take extra copies in case you would like to plan several different events or projects.

Briefly describe the project, saying who will benefit from it and in what ways.

When and where will it happen?

List the key people involved and their roles.

Do you need special permission? Do you need equipment or resources?

How will you notify the community about the event?

If you need to raise money to fund the event, how will you do this?

How will you decide if the project has been a success?

List any extra information you need, or add extra information about the project.

You may photocopy this page

Topic 3: Thinking about regular services

Human life is full of patterns, regular habits and routines. This can sometimes be oppressive, but routines also help us build and run our lives. Think about some of the routines in your own life and how they bring structure to it.

Worship employs time-honoured structures and patterns which become familiar over time. Every act of Christian worship contains some basic elements: welcome (Greeting); the reading of scripture (Ministry of the Word); prayers (Intercession); and sending out (Dismissal). There are often other elements too, such as hymns, anthems, communion and a sermon. For this topic, you are required to look at the structure of individual services (and how music forms a part of them) and use your findings to develop a service plan (Order of Service) of your own.

First, think about some regular services – either ones you attend for worship or ones in which your choir takes part, or both. You could look at several different types of service (for example, Morning prayer, Evening prayer or Eucharist/Communion/Mass) or choose one particular type and study a few examples of it. Look at the prayer book for the services you are describing.

Often the books only contain a few words and instructions, but in actual worship a lot more happens beyond this. Think about the various elements of worship: readings, prayers, blessings, acclamations, actions, music and so on. What gives each individual service its character? Describe each one on a separate piece of paper, referring to the points below.

- List the parts of the service in order, one after the other.

- For each part, say: *what* is happening; *whereabouts* in the church; *who* is involved; and *which* text or music is used (if any).

When you have described at least *four* services in this way, think about the general questions below and write your answers on a separate sheet.

- What elements were common to all the services?

- What patterns or structures were common to all?

- Were there any big differences between the services?

- Were there any distinctive or unusual elements?

- What was the particular role of the music in each service?

Now devise a short regular service of your own for one of these occasions: Advent; the Baptism of Christ; a Sunday in Lent; the day of Pentecost; or (if applicable) the Patronal Festival of your own church. Use a service book to help you with the basic structure, and add in the other elements yourself. For these you will need to look in the Bible, hymn books and other music resources, prayer or service books, collections of poetry and so on.

As you collect your ideas, you may also find it useful to talk to your choir trainer or other members of the choir or church. Use the worksheet opposite. If you like, take copies so that you can try this activity more than once.

1) Name the service and the season or festival.

2) Choose a passage of scripture (in your choice of translation) that is appropriate for this service, and say why it is suitable.

3) Write a suitable prayer, poem or piece of prose, and explain what you have written. It should be something you have created yourself. Include it on a separate piece of paper.

4) Select at least one suitable hymn or song for the congregation to sing, and explain your choice(s).

5) Select at least two suitable musical items which are not congregational hymns (for example a solo, a choral anthem or instrumental piece). Explain your choices.

Now list these items in the order they will appear in your service.

You may photocopy this page

Targets

 The targets for the Yellow level of *Voice for Life* are listed on pages 46–50. As you work through this book, you will learn to do all the things below. This section is a record of your progress, so write your name here.

 _____

Each time you achieve a target, your choir trainer will sign the box and record the date. There is no time limit to complete the targets. It is more important to learn everything thoroughly than to rush to finish the book. Your choir trainer will make sure that you make steady progress so that when you finish the book you are prepared for the next level.

When all the boxes are signed, you have successfully completed Yellow level. Your choir trainer will sign the declaration on the inside back cover of this book, where you can also find out what happens next.

Module A: Using the voice well
The singer understands the need for regular practice and:

	Signed:	Date:
• understands what makes good posture and is aware of the effects of bad posture on vocal production.		
• understands that posture helps prepare the mind for singing and is an important part of communication, and of presenting an image of confidence and professionalism.		
• understands the mechanics of breathing and uses this understanding to prepare the voice for singing.		
• sings with good breath support and is able to sing long notes and phrases with an even tone and without a decline of energy or support towards the end.		
• uses the back muscles to strengthen the sound		
• sings with resonance throughout the vocal range.		
• sings without tightening the jaw or pushing/crushing the larynx downwards.		
• blends the different registers of the voice and can move between them with agility.		
• sings with a variety of vocal tones.		

Module A *continued*

The singer:

	Signed:	Date:
• understands the difference between solo and choral singing. Contributes to the choral sound whilst blending the voice with the ensemble as a whole, without compromising good vocal technique.		
• sings with clear diction to create appropriate style and expression.		
• uses vowels to produce resonance, and ensures that consonants are clear without interrupting the flow of the tone.		
• has performed three contrasting pieces with a range of over an octave. These were sung from memory and demonstrated agility, good articulation and diction, good breath control and intonation, and a variety of vocal tone.		
• has sung confidently, accurately and musically a solo or solo line in a concert or service.		

MODULE B: Musical skills and understanding

The singer has completed the theory section of the Yellow workbook and demonstrates that he/she knows and understands:

	Signed:	Date:
• all key signatures, major and minor.		
• the difference between melodic and harmonic minor scales.		
• double sharps and double flats.		
• the characteristics and names of all intervals up to an octave, including diminished and augmented intervals.		
• the difference between primary and secondary chords, and how chords relate to a given key.		
• the difference between primary chords in root position, first and second inversion.		
• more complex chords (for example, chords with added 6th, 7th or 9th).		

Module B *continued*
The singer understands:

Signed: Date:

* the function of a cadence. The names and characteristics of perfect, imperfect, plagal and interrupted cadences.

* the time signatures 5/4, 5/8, 7/4 and 7/8.

* the concept of modes.

* the commonly used performance directions listed on pages 34–35.

Module B *continued*
The singer has read and understood the music theory in Module B and can:

Signed: Date:

* look at a short excerpt of music and
  i)   name the key signature (any key)
  ii) name any note in the first chord
  iii) name the first chord and its inversion
  iv) name the relation of the chord to the key
  v)   on hearing the first chord, sing any of its notes in their vocal range at the request of the choir trainer.

* sing any interval up to an octave above a given starting note.

* sing a minor scale (harmonic or melodic at the singer's choice) ascending and descending of one octave. The key chord and key note will first be sounded.

* identify the cadence (perfect, imperfect, plagal or interrupted) at the end of an extract of music.

* identify the time of a passage in 5/4, 5/8, 7/4 or 7/8. The passage of music will be played twice. The singer should then state the time signature.

* sight-read fluently a piece of moderate difficulty. The set piece may be in any key or time signature, and may include triplets, duplets, dotted notes, music in changing time signatures and syncopated rhythms.

MODULE C: Repertoire

The singer has completed the section on repertoire in the workbook and knows how to take a piece of music and:

	Signed:	Date:
• discuss the themes of the text and what it communicates.		
• describe how the composer has set the words (for example, syllabic, melismatic, repetition, word-painting).		
• discuss the composer's use of different colours and textures and how this reflects the text and affects the mood of the music.		
• look at the events of the composer's life, their historical/political background, and discuss any connections with his/her musical output.		
• discuss the characteristics of the musical period in which the composer lived.		
• name other pieces in the same genre and compare/contrast them.		
• discuss any performing conventions that would have affected the piece and compare this with how it is performed today.		

MODULE D: Belonging to the choir

The singer:

	Signed:	Date:
• is committed, reliable and punctual, always informing the choir trainer before being absent.		
• is an outstanding member of the choir, setting an excellent example to other singers through attendance, behaviour, commitment, and musical standards.		
• understands the delicate balance in a choir between giving a strong musical lead and blending with other singers.		
• understands that the choir is a team and the importance of participating in the practicalities of running the team, e.g. setting up rehearsal rooms, collecting music, etc.		
• takes responsibility for the less experienced singers.		

Targets

MODULE E: Choir in context

The singer has completed at least *one* of the three topics on pages 40–45

	Signed:	Date:
• Topic 1: The changing repertoire of our choir		
• Topic 2: Serving the wider community		
• Topic 3: Thinking about regular services		

Here your choir trainer may write extra information, comments abour your progress, or things to remember for the future. You may wish to add some notes of your own, too.

On these pages, you will find many of the signs and symbols you will see in the music you sing. You will already know many of them from earlier *Voice for Life* workbooks. Things that are newly explained in this book are shown below with a page number, which tells you where to find a more detailed explanation.

Simple time signatures

4 crotchet beats in a bar	4 crotchet beats in a bar	3 crotchet beats in a bar	2 crotchet beats in a bar	2 minim beats in a bar	2 minim beats in a bar
$\frac{4}{4}$	C	$\frac{3}{4}$	$\frac{2}{4}$	$\frac{2}{2}$	¢

Compound time signatures

In the compound time signatures shown below, each main beat is a dotted crotchet which divides into three quavers.

4 dotted crotchet beats in a bar (12 quavers)	3 dotted crotchet beats in a bar (9 quavers)	2 dotted crotchet beats in a bar (6 quavers)	1 dotted crotchet beat in a bar (3 quavers)
$\frac{12}{8}$	$\frac{9}{8}$	$\frac{6}{8}$	$\frac{3}{8}$

New time signatures (page 32)

In the time signatures shown below, the bar may be further divided into irregular sub-groups of two, three or four beats.

5 crotchet beats in a bar	5 quaver beats in a bar	7 crotchet beats in a bar	7 quaver beats in a bar
$\frac{5}{4}$	$\frac{5}{8}$	$\frac{7}{4}$	$\frac{7}{8}$

Tone and semitone patterns in scales and modes

Below you will find the interval patterns (ascending unless otherwise stated) of all the scales (page 21) and modes (page 33) you have learned so far. These will enable you to construct any scale or mode starting on any note. **T** = tone; **S** = semitone; **A** = augmented second (a tone plus a semitone)

Major scale
T–T–S–T–T–T–S

Harmonic minor scale
T–S–T–T–S–A–S

Melodic minor scale ascending
T–S–T–T–T–T–S

Melodic minor scale descending
T–T–S–T–T–S–T

Dorian mode
T–S–T–T–T–S–T

Phrygian mode
S–T–T–T–S–T–T

Lydian mode
T–T–T–S–T–T–S

Mixolydian mode
T–T–S–T–T–S–T

Aeolian mode
T–S–T–T–S–T–T

Reference

The circle of keys

This chart shows all the major and minor keys and their key signatures. As you move clockwise by step around the circle, the key signatures increase by one sharp. As you move anti-clockwise, they increase by one flat. Sharp and flat meet at the bottom of the circle: F sharp major (six sharps) is the same key as G flat major (six flats) – see page 19.

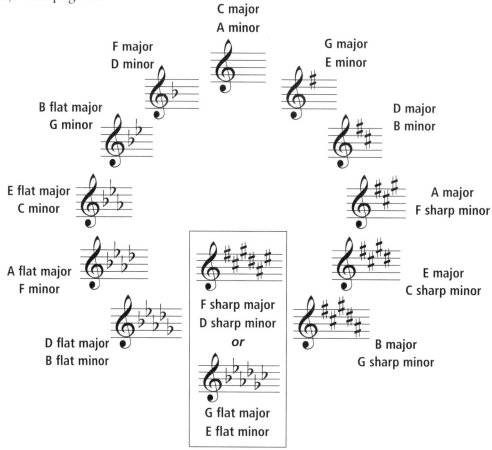

Primary and secondary chords (page 27)

Primary chords are the tonic (I), the subdominant (IV) and the dominant (V). All the others are secondary chords.

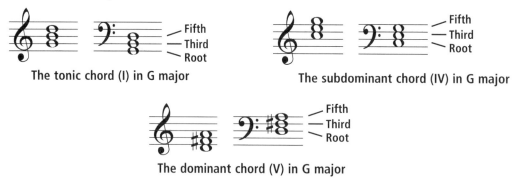

The tonic chord (I) in G major

The subdominant chord (IV) in G major

The dominant chord (V) in G major

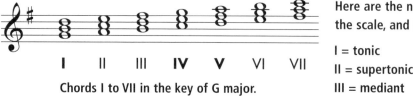

Chords I to VII in the key of G major.
The primary chords are shown in **bold** type

Here are the names of the notes of the scale, and their triads

I = tonic	V = dominant
II = supertonic	VI = submediant
III = mediant	VII = leading-note
IV = subdominant	

Chords in inversion (page 29)

Example 1:
In C major in
the treble clef:

Root position
(root at the bottom)

First inversion
(third at the bottom)

Second inversion
(fifth at the bottom)

Example 2:
In A minor in
the bass clef:

Root position
(root at the bottom)

First inversion
(third at the bottom)

Second inversion
(fifth at the bottom)

More complex chords (page 30)

Example 1:
In C major in
the treble clef:

Dominant seventh
chord

Tonic with an
added sixth

Tonic with an
added ninth

Example 2:
In F major in
the bass clef:

Dominant seventh
chord

Tonic with an
added sixth

Tonic with an
added ninth

Cadences (page 31)
In G major

Perfect cadence

V   I

Dominant   Tonic

Imperfect cadence

IV   V

Subdominant   Dominant

Imperfect cadence

I   V

Tonic   Dominant

Plagal cadence

IV   I

Subominant   Tonic

Imperfect cadence

V   V

Dominant   Submediant

Intervals

Here are the intervals you have learned to sing and recognize so far in *Voice for Life*, in ascending order of size, in the treble and bass clefs.

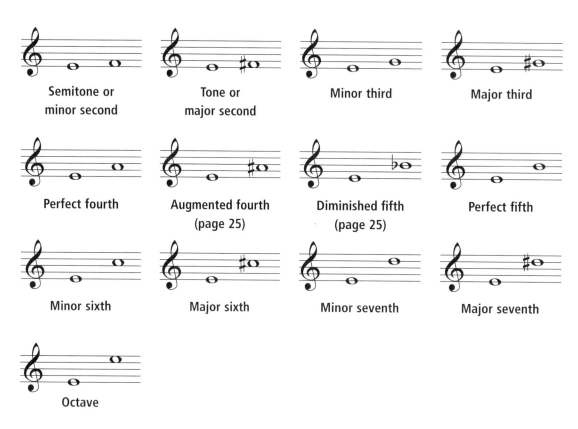

Semitone or minor second   Tone or major second   Minor third   Major third

Perfect fourth   Augmented fourth (page 25)   Diminished fifth (page 25)   Perfect fifth

Minor sixth   Major sixth   Minor seventh   Major seventh

Octave

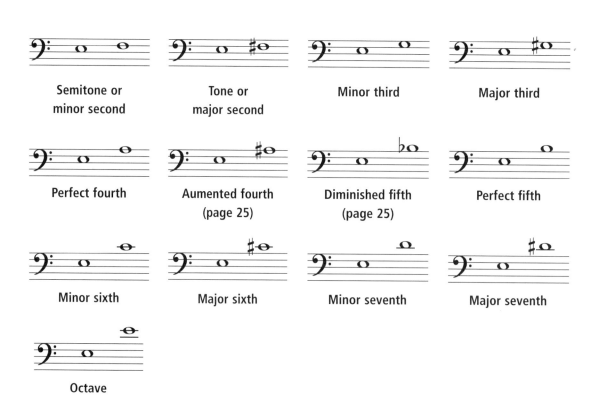

Semitone or minor second   Tone or major second   Minor third   Major third

Perfect fourth   Aumented fourth (page 25)   Diminished fifth (page 25)   Perfect fifth

Minor sixth   Major sixth   Minor seventh   Major seventh

Octave

Important words used in this book are explained briefly here. For a more detailed explanation, go to the pages listed under each heading. Any word in **bold** type also has an entry elsewhere in this index.

Aspirated onset a way to begin singing a note. There is air movement first, followed by the vibration of the **vocal folds**   15

Attendance   39

Augmented made bigger; an augmented **interval** is one which has a semitone added   25

Augmented fourth an **interval** which is one semitone larger than a perfect fourth   25

Back muscles   8

Balance   5

Breathing   6–8

Cadence a group of chords at the end of a phrase or section of music   31, 53

Choral singing   39

Clothing (for performance)   18

Composers   36–38

Consonants   14, 15

Diaphragm the main muscle used in **inhalation**   6–7

Diction   14–16

Diminished made smaller; a diminished **interval** is one which has a semitone taken away   25

Diminished fifth an **interval** which is one semitone smaller than a perfect fifth   25

Diphthong two vowel sounds which are pronounced as one syllable   16

Dominant the fifth note of a scale   27

Dominant chord (or dominant triad) a chord based on the **dominant** note of a scale   27

Dominant seventh chord a chord based on the **dominant** with an added minor seventh above the **root**   30

Double flat a sign which indicates that the note it precedes is to be lowered by two semitones   23

Double sharp a sign which indicates that the note it precedes is to be raised by two semitones   23

Exhalation breathing out   6

Falsetto   13

First inversion a chord is in first inversion when the third note of the **triad** is the lowest note   29

Glottal onset (or **glottal stop**) this happens when the **vocal folds** vibrate first, and air movement follows   15

Harmonic minor a minor scale in which the ascending and descending versions are identical   51

Imperfect cadence a **cadence** which ends with a **dominant chord**   31, 53

Inhalation breathing in   6

Intensity   7

Internet   36

Interrupted cadence a **cadence** which ends on the **submediant chord**   31, 53

Interval the distance in pitch between two notes   25–26, 54

Inversion the position of the notes of a **triad** in relation to the **root**   29

Larynx the area of the neck and throat where vocal sound is produced   9–11

Melodic minor a minor scale in which the ascending and descending versions are different   21, 51

Mode a type of scale   33, 51

Mood   37-38

Nasal tone a vocal tone which is produced by singing through the nose as well as the mouth   11, 12

Perfect cadence a **cadence** which consists of a **dominant chord** followed by a **tonic chord**   31, 53

Performance   17

Performance conventions   38

Plagal cadence a **cadence** which consists of a **subdominant chord** followed by a **tonic chord**   31, 53

Index